THE HUMPBACK'S TAIL

By the same author

Poetry for children
The Listening Station
Now You See Me, Now You …
*I Don't Want an Avocado for an
Uncle*

Poetry for adults
A Path of Rice
Pilot
Armature
I'll Dress One Night as You

Short stories
Family Connections

Radio Plays
Poles Apart
Starved for Love
Life Assurance
Dinner in the Iguanodon

THE HUMPBACK'S WAIL

Poems by

Chrissie Gittins

Illustrations by Paul Bommer

Rabbit Hole Publications

for the children of Lewisham

First published in 2010
by Rabbit Hole Publications
24 Elsinore Road, London SE23 2SL

Designed by LOUP
Printed by Diamond, Dartford

Some of the poems in the this book have
appeared in/on:
Dulwich Living (2008)
Laugh Out Loud (Macmillan, 2008)
BBC Radio Suffolk (2009)
Bards in the Bog (Shetland Libraries, 2009)
A Time to Speak (Schofield & Sims, 2010)

To My Daughter, As She Learns to Play the Qin
was commissioned by Barbican Education
in 2009

With special thanks to Paul Bommer,
Carys Davies, Keith Deal, Dean Pavitt and
Esther Cooper-Gittins.

CONTENT

THE HUMPBACK'S WAIL
for Gothic Mede Lower School, Arlesey

For twenty hours I sing my song,
my body arched, my head hung down.
I sing for her to come along
and swim up close beside me.

She'll love my sound,
my clicks and squeaks,
my lilting moans,
my squeals and creaks.

She'll immediately appreciate
the trouble I take
to vary my song
as it flows through the deep.

Barnacled like me,
she'll have lumps and bumps,
a slip-slapping tail
and a wild beauty.

We'll stay in warm waters
while our baby is born.
Come to me soon,
don't leave me lovelorn.

SUZANNAH THE TAIL WAGGER

soar.
spirits
their
make
to
way
fire
sure
a
is
wag
tail
a
blue,
feeling
is
them
of
one
If
labrador.
beloved
her
of
tail
the
wags
wagger
tail
the
Suzannah

MOON JELLY FISH, HORNIMAN MUSEUM

Handkerchiefs of jelly fish
flex across azure blue,
sculling up the tank
like fragile umbrellas
cowed against a storm.

Pulsing downwards,
followed by clouds of ribbon legs,
their mushroom rims
fold open, fold closed.

Hung with a string of fibre optics
they turn inside-out, ragged,
hovering next to each other
to puzzle over the lack of shore.

NIGHT SKY IN THE CLUN VALLEY
for Vincent

The sky is throwing out woks,
The moon is munching bananas,
The stars wear sparkly socks,
The planets are harbouring llamas.

KASSANDRA

Kassandra is my silent friend,
she doesn't know how to speak,
she smiles and sticks her tongue out
and dances down the street.

Her hair is spun like candy floss,
her skin is ivory white,
she runs across the playground,
jumping like a kite.

The other day I asked her,
if she had a wish or three,
What would she want?
What would she wish?
What would she want to be?

She stood there in amazement,
she spun around three times,
she came to a halt,
knelt down on the ground
and drew pictures in the sand.

First she drew a wide sun,
its rays long and strong,
then she drew a reindeer
dragging a sledge along.

Then she drew a lily,
its petals curved and sleek,
then she drew a mountain
with a tall spiky peak.

Last she drew a little girl
standing by a tree,
she pointed at the little girl,
then pointed straight at me.

THE RETURN OF THE WILDMAN OF ORFORD

Was I a wildman or was I a merman?
Did I have whiskers or was it a tail?
None of this matters, since 1167
I've learnt to be strong,
as strong as a whale.

Back then I was caught
in nets with the fishes,
I floundered with flounder,
was mocked by a haddock,
I laughed at the soul of a Dover sole.

Strung up by my feet
you questioned my silence.
I ask you – how could I speak
of the deep to those who don't know
that the sea is darker than a December night,
that the sea is deeper than amethyst,
that the sea can wrap you in an iron clasp,
that the sea can whisper, and the sea can rasp?

You let me swim between lines of nets,
I dipped and dived and found my way free.
For 800 years I've soared the waves,
never been caught, been allowed to be.

I'm back to tell you I'm neither
merman nor monster,
nor a fiend nor a ghoul.
I'm the spirit of the sea.
And I'm nobody's fool.

*The Merman of Orford is said to have appeared
in or around 1167.*

WHEN I TRAVELLED FROM THE COUNTRY TO THE CITY
for Carol

When I travelled from the country to the city
the wind remained in my veins,

the heather spread through my fingers,
the moor sprawled over my back.

The quilted hillside was heavy
when I lay beneath it to rest,

my dreams were of rivers and valleys,
of a sky streaming east to west.

SPRING WEATHER

I woke in the night
to WHOOSHING,
THRASHING,
and CRASHING.

The windows rattled,
the door shook –
a wind so loud
it could have been
a storm at sea
for Captain Hook.
But this was a holiday
in Mallorca!

I took a sheet,
wedged it in the door,
but still the wind soared,
all night it raged
like a giant angry with fever.

This wind flew in from the Sahara,
from swirling dunes of roasting sand.

It made me long
for flurries of snow,
it was the hot, the fierce, the very dry
Sirocco.

GREY HERON, CRYSTAL PALACE DINOSAUR PARK

Broken black streaks
feather his throat,

black eyebrows shoot
into a Mandarin's moustache.

Eyes staring ahead,
rigid as the cement pterodactyl

in flight to his right,
head darts down.

He straightens with a fish in his beak,
slowly gulping,

like sucking
on a saved caramel.

MY FRIEND BOB
for Barlby Primary School, North Kensington

My friend Bob
is always there,
he doesn't turn
a single hair
if I'm lonely or sad,
or if I wake like a bear
with a very sore head.

My friend Bob
is loyal and true,
wherever I go –
to the park, or the zoo,
he comes too.
We see penguins waddle
and the lions being fed.

He tells me how
to play the game,
when to dribble,
when to shoot,
when to pass the ball.
If I score he cheers
loudest of all,
till my poor round face
goes tomato red.

My friends all know about
my friend Bob,
they ask how he is,
and who is his Dad?
He doesn't have a home,
he lives with me.
He has a very comfy place
inside my head!

BIRDS I

a murmuration of starlings
became
a clattering of choughs

a quarrel of sparrows
gave way to
a squabble of seagulls

despite
a scolding of jays
what followed was
a murder of crows

THE FRAGRANT PIRATE
for Westcott First School near Dorking

You can't let your standards slip on ship,
there may be rats and a bilge water stench,
but I take care to always indulge
in a little late night pampering.

The sun and wind play havoc with my skin,
so when the lights go dim at eight
I smooth my face with a very large tin
of soothing yellow lanolin.

As the hulk creaks and my shipmates snore,
we rock and roll with the waves.
I rub my feet with jasmine oil,
just as my fourteenth wife did on shore.

Lavender and musk are a must
to inhale after hours of smoke from cannons,
I pour three drops on my sack of a pillow –
sound sleep will surely follow?

*Lanolin is a fatty substance found on sheep's wool
which is used in moisturizer*

I WANT TO BE MY BABY BROTHER

I want to waddle without a nappy,
neatly miss my potty.
I want smears of marmite round my mouth.

I want you to blow raspberries on my belly,
suck my fingers, throw me in the air.
I want a currant biscuit in each hand,

another crunched in the carpet,
crispy crumbs between my toes.
I want to sit in the bath with a tipper,

I want to pull the leaves off lilies,
I want to lie on your back
with my head in the dip of your neck.

I want to scream so loud when I can't catch
the butterfly that your ears hurt.

MY OLDER BROTHER
for Esther

My brother jumps on me,
pushes me,
pulls me,
hits me,
shouts at me,
rolls me over.

He kisses me,
cuddles me,
reads me stories,
makes me laugh - ha ha ha.
Makes me cry.

Then buys me a bracelet from his school trip to Wales.

THE BEST HIDING PLACE IN THE WORLD

I'm crouching in my hiding place,
my mum is going wild,
she's traipsing up and down the aisles,
"Where are you, naughty child?"

I'm counting up the soap powders –
the liquid and the blocks,
they line the shelves opposite,
they clean my jeans and socks.

Mum's voice is getting louder,
the manager gets called,
he sends a message to the store,
(he's tall and very bald).

"If you see a little girl,
dressed in a purple top,
please inform the manager,
then our search can stop."

Game's up, I'm caught –
been seen through the holes,
I'm hiding on the bottom shelf –
behind the toilet rolls!

WASP ON THE TUBE

If I knew how I got here
I wouldn't have commmmmmmmmme,

those doors banged shut,
that was the end of my funnnnnnnnnnnn,

I'm buzzing around
and causing a hummmmmmmmmmmm,

they're all looking up
and they think I am dummmmmmmmmb.

I want to escape,
get back to the sunnnnnnnnnnnnnnnnnnn,

that boy's going mad
and grabbing his Mummmmmmmmmmm,

if we weren't in a tunnel
I know they'd all runnnnnnnnnnnnnnnnnn,

at last, King's Cross,
my tube journey's donnnnnnnnnnnnnnnne.

GLORIOUS FOOD

I like Sunday dinner,
I like beans on toast,
I like egg and soldiers,
I like pasta most
with Ragu sauce and tuna.

Best is Sunday roast.

SUMMER PUDDING
for Carol

The pudding of summer
bursts on my tongue
like the glisten of sun on the sea.

The grit of the seeds is the sand
in my toes, and the sand
which sticks to my knee.

The red of the juice
is the blood on my leg
when I fell on a stone on the shore.

In the sharp days of winter
I'll remember the berries,
the running and splashing,

the skimming and swimming,
wanting more and more and more.

MAKING CREAM CAKES FOR TINA TURNER

It was a dream I had last week.
She phoned to say the paper got it wrong -
'If you want to look good, you have to
care about yourself, eat brown rice,
steamed vegetables, and dance.'

In fact she adores pavlova and crème brûlée,
she'd die for trifle with real custard,
nothing beats a blackcurrant tart
crusted with castor sugar.

Her absolute favourites are a mousse
so full of chocolate that the spoon stands up,
and a rhubarb crumble gone rock solid the next day.

MOUNTAIN BIKER POSTER
for Sam

I used to jump the pavement,
do wheelies in the air,
but now I'm in a photograph
and I just sit and stare.

My feet won't touch the tarmac,
the handle-bars are turned,
my gloves have melted on my hands
and my nose is rather burned.

POSTCARD FROM THE BATHROOM

I'm on holiday in my bathroom,
the sun is streaming in,
the air lock in the water pipes
makes an awful din.

I'm lying in hot water
with ice cream down my chin,
racing my clockwork terrapins –
I know which one will win.

Mum's making tuna sandwiches
with bread cut really thin,
she hands them on a plastic plate
with a cheeky seaside grin.

It's better than Ibiza,
no queuing for check-in,
just lie back in my steamy pool,
rivers in my skin.

IRIS UPSIDAISY

Iris Upsidaisy has corkscrew curls,
they're corn-yellow spinning coils,
they twist and they whirl.

They twist around the library,
they twist along the street,
they twist up lamp posts
and round the shoppers' feet.

They whirl along telegraph wires
and up the traffic lights,
they curl around chestnut trees
on cold and windy nights.

They spin along her forehead,
they bounce up and down,
they shake when she laughs out loud,
they hide a puzzled frown.

When her curls are resting
on her pillow while she sleeps,
they straighten out and stretch themselves
then lie around in heaps.

Iris wakes in the morning
and her curls curl up again,
they dance with glee for all to see,

her jitterbugging mane.

the jitterbug: a fast dance performed to swing music,
popular in the 1940's

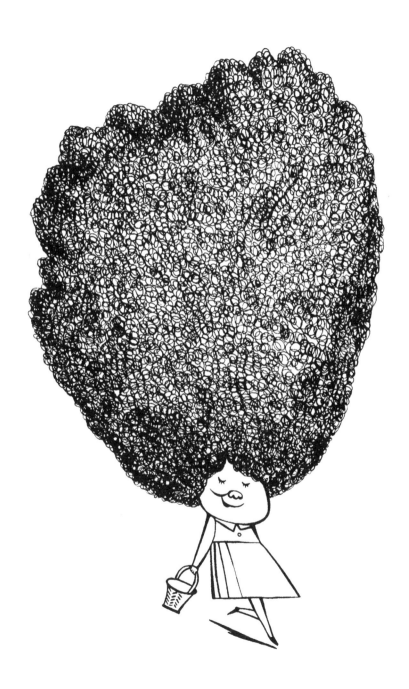

I LIKE THE TASTE OF COMPUTERS
for Oldfield Park Infants, Bath

I like the taste of computers,
I like the feel of the sky,
I like the sound of potatoes,
I like the look of a sigh.

I like the smell of windows,
the feel of a wide rainbow,
I like the taste of winter,
and the sound of thick deep snow.

THE RED ROBOT AND THE RABBIT

The red robot and the rabbit
met down a leafy lane.

"I've got rhubarb in my rucksack,"
said the robot to the rabbit.

"I can't eat that," said the rabbit,
"it gives me such a pain."

"I've got a rocket in *my* rucksack,"
said the rabbit to the robot.

"Let's launch it from the footpath
and make a racket in the rain."

The rocket rose up to the heavens
and spread sparkles all about.

Said the robot to the rabbit,
"Can you do that again?"

LITTLE PEOPLE

There are little people in my bed,
I hear them every night.

They march along my pillow,
and swing on my reading light.

They're always there in the morning
when my eyes blink up and down.

Half of them have a silly smile,
the other half, a frown.

If I smile at the frowning half
they start to wriggle and squiggle.

If I laugh a belly laugh,
they giggle, and giggle,
and giggle, and giggle
and giggle.

There are little people in my bed,
I hear them every night.

We all go to sleep together,
with our eyes shut tight.

THE INSIDE-OUT TEACHER

She wore her jumper inside-out,
we could all see the seams,
it had to stay the whole day long
or she would not see her dreams.

She wore her belt the wrong way round,
with the buckle at the back,
sitting on an upright chair
it gave her back a crack.

She wore her smile upside-down,
to make the children giggle,
they ran off to the playground
with a wriggle and a wiggle.

ROUNDABOUT

I'm sitting still
on the roundabout,
the trees are all a blur,

the slide and swings
spin into one,
I can hear a gentle whirr.

The clouds are rushing
through the sky,
like pillows on a stick.

Two boys
are playing football.
Kick, kick, kick.

The ice cream van
comes round three times!
Which flavour will I choose?

A strawberry cone?
A Ninety-Nine?
Or a lolly made from juice?

Two girls
are on the climbing frame,
they've nearly reached the top.

I've been spinning,
spinning, spinning round.
My head says it's time to stop!

CORMORANT

You'll know me from my hooked beak,
my beady eyes, the way I hang my wings
to dry. I stand on a post in the lake,
relish the breeze rustling my feathers.

You'd think my wings were waterproof –
I spend so much time submerged,
but I rather like hanging around
after a surge through waves and rain.

I can ponder the state of the nation,
watch walkers walking their muts.
If I didn't have this quiet time,
I'd go completely nuts!

DID I MISS SOMETHING?

I'm a fully trained dodologist,
I studied with the best –
their habitat, their preferences,
I never failed a test.

I know what they like to eat –
fruit fallen from a palm,
they cannot fly above the ground,
so sometimes come to harm.

They like to bathe and swim along
in their country of Mauritius,
I went there with my instruments,
my trip was not auspicious.

I searched the country inch by inch,
for as long as I could bear,
no matter how hard I looked –

I found no dodos anywhere.

A SLEW OF CLERIHEW

Tutankhamun

Tutankhamun
Died too soon,
He lay in the Valley of Kings
Surrounded by golden things.

Queen Victoria

Queen Victoria
Was bursting with euphoria
When Prince Albert's ambition
Produced the Great Exhibition.

Henry VIII

Henry the Eighth
Had very bad breath,
That's why every wife
Had a very short life.

William Shakespeare

William Shakespeare
Showed no fear,
He killed off his leading men
So they couldn't come back again.

TO MY DAUGHTER,
AS SHE LEARNS TO PLAY THE QIN
(from 'Feeling from Mountain and Water',
an animated Chinese film by Te Wei)

I will teach you as I was taught.

An old man came down the mountain,
leaning in the wind.
I caught him when he stumbled.

His music met mine, he lay his qin before me.
Orange leaves feathered the air,
by snowfall I could play.

When the frog swelled his chest and
fishes gathered at a worm
we left to sail the slanting gorge.

Monkeys jumped in trees,
stones split falling water.
I didn't want to say goodbye.

I clutched him close,
then knelt and took the qin
bequeathed to me.

He left as he had come.
From up on high I plucked the strings,
filled the valley with his gift.

I will teach you well, as I was taught.

Qin: (pronounced 'chin') a plucked 7-string Chinese
musical instrument of the zither family.

THE HORNIMAN LION

There's a lion in the middle of our zoo,
he stalks around not knowing what to do,
he's waiting for a day –
a sunny day in May,
when he can sashay to his Mum's in Katmandu.

INGREDIENTS FOR COOKING

A pinch of patience,
a huge dollop of planning,
a tablespoon of shopping,
a good slosh of time,
and 500 grams of luck.

FOOD SENSE

What I like about the smell of food is
chicken roasting in the oven.

What I like about the sound of food is
onions frying in a pan.

What I like about the feel of food is
a shiny apple in my hand.

What I like about the look of food is
strawberries, raspberries and blueberries
piled high in my bowl.

What I like about the taste of food is
popping popcorn,
tingly ice cream,
salty chips,
crunchy carrots,
slimy yoghurt,
wobbly jelly,
and long long strands of slippy slurpy spaghetti.

BIRDS II

a bouquet of pheasants
was given to
a charm of finches

a wisp of snipe
spooled over
a ballet of swans

a rafter of turkeys
bumped into
a herd of wrens

a paddling of ducks
was drowned by
a descent of woodpeckers

a deceit of lapwings
recognized
an unkindness of ravens

a siege of herons
superseded
a dread of terns

a vein of goldfinches
was sold in
a bazaar of guillemots

a convocation of eagles
winked at
a stare of owls

BOXES AT CHAPEL STREET MARKET

for Winton Primary School, King's Cross

Cheery tomatoes,
cherry tomatoes,
smiling to each other,
reflecting the sun in their
redness.

Hairy coconuts,
hairy coconuts,
a nose, and two eyes
looking out
at the crowd.

Bitter melon,
bitter melon,
green and spiky
scary hedgehogs
hooking up together.

Pak choi, pak choi,
packed tight
snuggling up till
they stir for a fry.

Ginger, ginger, ginger,
knobbly, like finger joints,
ready to flavour soup.

Oranges, oranges
piled high from heated Egypt,
their dimply skin ripe
for your thumb.

LOU'S PYJAMA-UNIFORM

It was cold when Lou got ready for bed,
it was warm in her school uniform,
she couldn't see the point of taking it off
to shiver in her bed till dawn.

So she pulled her nightie over the top
and climbed into her bed,
her Mum was gone to work by seven,
so nothing was ever said.

Until one day her headteacher
dragged Lou into her room.
"Why is your uniform so crumpled,
do you not have an iron at home?"

"We do have an iron," said Lou in defence,
"but it's cold at home in my room,
so I sleep inside my uniform."
Lou let out a huge wide yawn.

"Doesn't your mother tell you off?"
"On no, she sees my nighty.
I put it on over the top,
then pray to God Almighty."

Lou's Mum was phoned straight away,
she came into school for a meeting.
Lou now has a new smooth uniform,
and her house has central heating.

CHEESY
for Pearl

When I was two
I didn't like Shropshire Blue.

Now I'm three
I like brie.

When I'm four
I'm going to eat more –

chippings of cheddar,
clumps of feta,
cobwebs of creamy mozzarella.

And when the wind blows a gale
I shall curl in my chair,

and nibble a piece
of whiter than white
Wensleydale.

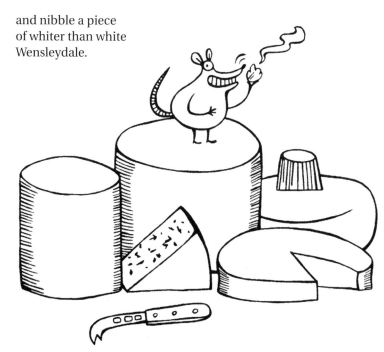

MY DAD'S MORE EMBARRASSING THAN YOUR DAD

My Dad's more embarrassing than your Dad.
Does yours get your friends' names wrong?

My Dad has to be more embarrassing than your Dad.
Does yours try to sing your favourite song?

My Dad is way more embarrassing than your Dad.
Does yours wear sandals with socks on the sands?

My Dad is so more embarrassing than your Dad.
Does yours dance with just his feet and his hands?

My Dad is definitely more embarrassing than your Dad.
Does yours ask you how to use the computer?

My Dad is a trillion times more embarrassing than your Dad.
Does yours try to wiggle his hooter?

DAWN MEETS THE QUEEN

The chandeliers were like upside-down sparkly trees,
the sofas were as long as stretch limousines.

I sunk, waist-deep, in red carpet,
nibbled miniature scones.

Watched by her Rembrandt and Vermeer
the Queen came near. She smiled.

"And which school are you from?
Are you enjoying your visit?"

I ran to my teacher.
"I've just spoken to THE QUEEN!"

My mouth was as wide as Japan.
"Really, she's *just* like my Nan!"

AMAZING MAISIE

Maisie was proper blazing
to be stuck all day in her pram.
She screamed and screamed
while she sat and watched
her Mum eating posh crisps
and ham.

It wasn't until her plane of a pram
was turned towards the trees,
that she bucked up and hushed up
and let out a ripple of smiles.

THE WAY HE USED TO BE

I miss the way my brother used to be,
he'd flop back on the sofa,
somersault on the lawn,

he punched the air,
gave me high five
when he won the football game.

All of a sudden
he'd clear the living room,
push back the table,

put on rock music
and wiggle his bottom from side to side.
I laughed till I cried.

He painted wicked pictures
with robots and kangaroos,
he held my hand

when we crossed the road,
he never let me loose
at snap or dominos.

I miss the way my brother used to be,
the way he stuck out his tongue,
the way he cuddled me.

NECKLACE
for Wanstead Church School

I had a row with my mum,
stormed off up the stairs,
I really was sorry
to make her worry,
staying out late
without a word.

I tidied my room
and cleaned the shoes,
and made my own packed lunch.
I picked her flowers
and swept the floor
and then I had a hunch.

I could mend her broken necklace,
the one her grandma gave.
I threaded the beads one by one
and counted off the days.

The day we rode on donkeys,
rattling down the beach,
the day she made me chocolate cake
and hid it out of reach,

the day she smoothed my forehead,
when a fever raged inside,
the day I held an egg and spoon
and she cheered me on with pride.

I gave my mum the necklace,
she wrapped her arms around.
In that delectable moment,
you could not hear a sound.

CASCADE

I keep kicking my football
over the fence,
the man next door gets annoyed.
When I ask for it back
he pretends it is lost –
he's a man we often avoid.

After loosing six balls
my parents said
they wouldn't buy any more.
How can I practise
and hone my skills
so at school I can finally score?

On Monday last week
I was kicking my heels
when my neighbour next door he calls,
"Look what I've found"
and over the fence
came a cascade of six red balls.

TIMING IS EVERYTHING

There's a time to tell your friend he's doing good,
And a time to tell your friend he's doing wrong.
There's time to eat broccoli,
And a time to eat milk chocolate.
There's a time to laugh out loud,
And a time to cry inside.
There's a time to wear a sparkly dress,
And a time to wear torn jeans.
There's a time to keep your favourite toy,
And a time to give it away.
There's a time to dance and jump and sing,
And a time to sit quietly and think.
There's a time to be angry and row,
And a time to make up and hug.
There's a time to a sow a seed and watch it grow,
And a time to harvest its fruits.

THE SIX DAYS OF ARVON
for Hayes School

On Monday I rode the tiger of my fear,
On Tuesday I beat the pulp of my anger,
On Wednesday I shook the feathers on my indecision,
On Thursday I drank the milk of my content,
On Friday I sang the goose music of success,
On Saturday I slid in the mud of wild delight.

FRUIT BAT

Ellie is a fruit bat,
she sits with her plate
sucking on a peach stone,
slurping at a fig.
Her paper thin wings
curl around her body,
her huge red eyes are ready
for dusk, for the flimsy
light of twilight.
She plops her plate
in the washing up bowl
then flies upstairs,
ready for a day
of hanging upside down.
She dreams of ripe bananas,
slushy avocados,
the squish and squash
of an orange mango.

THE VERY FORTUNATE FROG

I live in a rubber tub,
it's a very fancy home,
my ceiling's made of lily pads,
I really cannot moan.

At night I go for a wander,
slurp up a worm or two,
flick on a fly, and wonder why,
some frogs live in a zoo.

For pudding I like a slug,
slimy and black as coal,
I lick my lips and open my mouth
and swallow my captive whole.

I plan on living for forty years,
squelching in the mud,
basking in the morning sun,
if I could dance a jig I would.

On hot days in July,
when I'm feeling sleepy-snoozie,
a hose pipe fills my fancy home,
and turns it into a jacuzzi.

FOR CHRISTMAS

I give you a wooden gate
to open onto the world,

I give you a bendy ruler
to measure the snow that swirls,

I give you a prestidigitator
to make your woes disappear,

I give you a hopping robin –
he'll be your friend throughout the year,

I give you a box of mist
to throw over past mist-akes,

I give you a slice of ice
to slide on mysterious lakes.

LULLABY

Forget about your homework,
forget about that fight,
give it up to the cheesy moon
and the meteor showers of night.

Chuck your frustrations out of the window,
punch your pillow with your fright,
then lie in a river of watercress,
tomorrow will be alright.

CHRISSIE GITTINS was born in Lancashire and lives in South London. Her children's poems have been broadcast on BBC Radio 4, animated for Cbeebies television and widely anthologized. *Now You See Me, Now You* ... was shortlisted for the first CLPE Poetry Award in 2003. Her second children's poetry collection *I Don't Want an Avocado for an Uncle* was shortlisted for the CLPE Poetry Award 2007 and was a Poetry Book Society Choice for the Children's Poetry Bookshelf; it was also chosen for the Boys into Books School Library Association booklist in 2008. In 2010 the republished *Now You See Me, Now You* ... was a PBS Choice for the Children's Poetry Bookshelf for the Spring Term.

Two of Chrissie's children's poems won Belmont Poetry Prizes in 2002. She has read her children's poetry at the Aldeburgh Poetry Festival, the Edinburgh International Book Festival, the Hay Festival and the Poets House in New York. Her residencies include twelve Southwark primary schools, an international school in Bangkok, the Refugee Council, and rural schools in Norfolk and the Highlands. In 2010 she was appointed Lewisham Borough's first Writer-in-Residence.

Chrissie also writes radio drama, and has published two poetry collections and a collection of short stories for adults. She tutors for the Arvon Foundation and is a member of the Poetry Society's Poetryclass team.

The Humpback's Wail is a Poetry Book Society Choice for the Children's Poetry Bookshelf, Summer Term 2010.
www.chrissiegittins.co.uk

PAUL BOMMER is an illustrator, graphic designer and printmaker, based in east London. He is a graduate of the National College of Art and Design (NCAD), Dublin. Paul finds inspiration everywhere, in the work of other artists past and present and in the world all around him – from illuminated Medieval manuscripts, folk art, pub signs and 18th century woodcuts, to the work of Edwards Lear and Bawden, and Czech book and poster design of the 60s and 70s. His clients include The Guardian, Reader's Digest, Harrods, Virgin, Scholastic Books, Which?, Saga, Cartoon Network and Slinky Pictures.
www.paulbommer.com